Teaching and Learning
Key Stage 2
Differentiated Activity Book

Sentence

Literacy

Year 6

Contents

Introduction

Differentiated Activity Books:

- support the teaching of the Literacy Hour
- help meet the majority of the objectives of the National Literacy Strategy Framework
- contain 30 units of work, sufficient for one school year
- are straightforward and easy to use
- have a clear teaching focus
- contain differentiated activities for each objective at foundation, intermediate and challenging levels of difficulty.

Features of the sentence Level Teaching Units

Teaching objective

Unit number

Teaching focus

Differentiated activity – foundation level

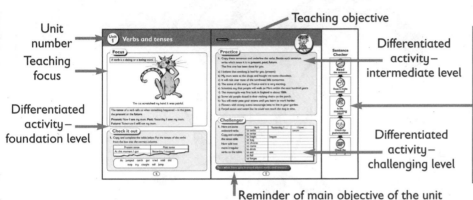

Differentiated activity – intermediate level

Differentiated activity – challenging level

Reminder of main objective of the unit

The fold out ready reference flap (inside back cover) provides children with a reminder of a consistently useful writing strategy which can always be applied to any piece of work.

Using the Differentiated Activity Books

A Variety of Uses

The books may be used to:
- introduce and teach individual National Literacy Strategy Framework objectives independently
- introduce individual National Literacy Strategy Framework objectives prior to studying them during Text Level work
- consolidate, develop and extend National Literacy Strategy Framework objectives studied during Text Level work
- provide work for whole class, group or individual work
- provide work for follow-up homework assignments.

Class Work

The Teaching focus provides a clear explanation of each objective with examples for discussion. Appropriate activities may be chosen from the range of differentiated tasks for discussion, or to work through, with the class.

Group and Individual Work

The Differentiated Activity Books are ideal for group and individual work. Work on the same objective may be realistically matched appropriately to individual children's abilities, allowing children to work independently.

Homework

The material in the books provides an ideal solution to meaningful homework assignments that can be differentiated appropriately for each pupil.

Focus

A **verb** is a **doing** or a **being** word.

The cat **scratched** my hand. It **was** painful.

The **tense** of a verb tells us when something happened — in the **past**, the **present** or the **future**.

Present: Now **I see** my mum. **Past:** Yesterday **I saw** my mum.
Future: Tomorrow **I will** see my mum.

Check it out

1. Copy and complete the table below. Put the tenses of the verbs from the box into the correct columns.

Present tense	Past tense
At this moment I got	Yesterday I stopped

do   jumped   catch   got   tried   told   did
stop   try   caught   tell   jump

Practice

1. Copy these sentences and underline the verbs. Beside each sentence, write which tense it is in: **present**, **past**, **future**.
The first one has been done for you.

a) I believe that smoking <u>is</u> bad for you. (present)
b) My mum went to the shops and bought me some chocolate.
c) It will rain over most of the northwest hills tomorrow.
d) The scene of this story is France and it is very exciting.
e) Scientists say that people will walk on Mars within the next hundred years.
f) The motorcycle was first built in England in about 1886.
g) Some old people dozed in their rocking chairs on the porch.
h) You will never pass your exams until you learn to work harder.
i) Flowers with strong scents encourage bees to live in your garden.
j) Farjad swam and swam but he could not reach the dog in time.

Challenger

1. Here are some awkward verbs. Copy and complete the tense table. Now add two more irregular verbs to the table.

Verb	Yesterday I …	I have …
to swim		swum
to write		
to begin	began	
to buy		
to choose		
to come		
to drink		
to eat	ate	
to fall		
to forget		

So – what have you learned about verbs and tenses?

Focus

A **verb is in the active** when the **subject** of the verb
is actually **performing the action** of the sentence.

Fred **drove** the new, red car.

Fred is the **subject** of the sentence.
He is the one performing the action. He is **driving** the car.

Check it out

1. Copy these sentences into your book. Underline the active verbs
and circle the subject of each sentence. The first one has been
done for you.

a) The (wind) <u>blew</u> strongly all night.

b) His appearance took me by surprise.

c) Suddenly, the door flew open.

d) My uncle grew the prize-winning tomatoes at the Show.

e) I told the gardener to cut the grass shorter this year.

f) The park warden hired extra staff to pick up the extra litter.

g) Gusts of wind made the candle-flame flicker mysteriously.

h) Shoppers crowded the streets in their rush to buy Christmas gifts.

Objectives ~ to understand the terms 'active' and 'passive'
~ to be able to transform a sentence from active to
passive, and vice versa

Practice

1. Copy these sentences and underline the verbs.

   Now rewrite the examples, changing the passive verb to an active one.

   Do it like this: **The car <u>was driven</u> by the priest – The priest <u>drove</u> the car.**

a) My luggage is inspected by the Customs Department.

b) The garage doors are operated by two guards.

c) I was guided to my seat by a young lady.

d) In our school nursery, children are looked after by Mrs Randall.

e) The glass was dropped by Robert.

f) The mouse was chased by the cat.

g) All the keys had been taken by someone.

h) The ball was kicked into the air by the girl.

Challenger

1. Rewrite this experiment, using only active verbs.

The test tube was taken by the teacher and was placed in the flame.
It was then heated until some bubbles in the water were seen. We were told
by Miss Sunhilla to keep out of the way as it might be dangerous. The
temperature of the liquid was taken by the teacher and was recorded in the
table. Then the liquid was left in a cold place in the classroom until it was
seen to change colour. While this was happening, the white solid was heated
in another part of the room. When this was seen to change colour also and
to give off a gas, the liquid and the solid were mixed together. Finally, the test
tube was washed out and was returned carefully to the shelf. By the time this
had happened, small blue crystals were seen to form. We were asked to
watch them until they grew to a large size. When the experiment was
complete we were allowed to hang the pretty crystals in the class.

So – what have you learned about active verbs?

Focus

A **verb is passive** when the action of the verb is being done to the subject by someone or something else in the sentence.
It often uses phrases such as **was** and **were**.

The car **was driven** by Fred.

The **car** is the **subject** of the sentence.
The verb **to drive** applies to the car and not to Fred.

Check it out

1. Copy these sentences. Underline the passive verbs and circle the subject. The first one has been done for you.

a) The (plate) was dropped by my brother.

b) The robber was taken by surprise when I fought back.

c) All the sweets were eaten by the children.

d) The assembly was finished with a prayer.

e) Our summer disco was organised by the teachers.

f) An exhibition of work was put on by Class 6.

g) Several books were thrown out of the bus by the naughty girls.

h) Three pieces of jewellery are being examined by the police for fingerprints.

Objectives ~ to understand the terms 'active' and 'passive'
~ to be able to transform a sentence from active to
passive, and vice versa

Practice

1. Copy the sentences below. Underline the verbs.

Now rewrite the examples. Change the active verb to a passive one.

Do it like this: **The priest <u>drove</u> the car – The car was <u>driven</u> by the priest.**

a) Thick wool carpets deadened the noise in the hall.

b) Radios direct the police to the crime.

c) In the store, glass lifts take customers to the top floor.

d) Our workshops carry out all kinds of car repairs.

e) Bad storms delayed the arrival of Concorde.

f) Large windows allow maximum light into the temple.

g) We chose a large green plant for the experiment.

h) The dogs chased the rabbits across the field.

Challenger

1. Rewrite these sentences. Change the passive verbs into active verbs.

For example; **A scream <u>was heard</u> by me in the classroom – I <u>heard</u> a scream in the classroom.**

a) Immediately, four children were running into the hallway and were disappearing out of the door.

b) But the children's panic was understood by the teacher.

c) His books were put down quietly and my friend was asked to find the Headteacher.

d) While he searched for the Headteacher, the rest of the class were asked to sit patiently.

e) The teacher was obeyed by the children and everything was fine when the four worried classmates were brought back in, crying.

f) The tissues were brought and the day was finished with an apology.

So – what have you learned about passive verbs?

Focus

Connectives are **words and phrases** which can **join together ideas**. Some of the commonest are **and**, **but**, **or**, **in other words**, **finally**, **nevertheless**, **just then**.

She was tired from swimming, **nevertheless** she helped her mum in the shop.

Check it out

1. Copy these sentences in your book and underline the connectives. The first one has been done for you.

a) They could go to the theme park <u>or</u> to the circus.

b) We will not arrive until after dinner, in other words, we will be late.

c) Sarah can come to stay but she will have to sleep in the spare room.

d) I would like the soup to start and the steak as my next course.

e) The clown spun around in circles, finally ending the show with a bow.

f) Let's not have a drink here because it's too crowded.

g) Jemila was complaining about the food until the manager came.

h) We drove to visit John before we had lunch.

i) I was just reading my book when there was a knock at the door.

Practice

1. Join each of these pairs of sentences using **and**, **but** or **so** to make single sentences.

a) The driver saw the danger sign. He slowed down.

b) The streets of New York were alive. The buildings were brilliantly lit.

c) The sun was shining brightly. There was a slight breeze.

d) I have a Siamese cat. She is called Cato.

e) The party started at seven o'clock. I did not arrive for an hour.

f) The TV programme was very exciting. Sarah was not home in time to watch it.

g) Her house was marked clearly on the map. We found it easily.

2. Use connectives such as **when, before**, **although**, **so that** to make each of these pairs of sentences into one.

a) Jason came to a halt. He spoke to me.

b) My computer was taken to the engineer. It needs to be made faster.

c) The girl screamed. The Great Dane barked at them.

d) The Russian athlete broke the world record. She was only thirteen.

Challenger

1. Write a suitable ending for each sentence using a connective.

a) The plane was waiting on the runway …

b) We placed the box …

c) After we placed the bread in the toaster …

d) She will give you the secret message on Monday in the park …

e) Yesterday, Mike took the wrong turning …

f) My mum walked into my bedroom …

g) All the money was …

So – what have you learned about connecting words and phrases?

Focus

Connectives are **words and phrases** which can **join together ideas**. Some of the commonest are **and**, **but**, **or**, **in other words**, **finally**, **nevertheless**, **just then**.

Jamil got top marks in the test, **in other words**, he came first.

Check it out

1. Copy these sentences in your book and underline the connectives.

a) The cat sat down and stretched in the sun.

b) All the birds were in the tree but they were quiet.

c) The birds all flew off, consequently the cat had no reason to be there.

d) She felt angry and flung the toy mouse into the air.

e) Tibbles walked away, firstly looking both ways for enemies.

f) Her garden was empty, but she was still on guard.

g) She was not really hungry, nevertheless she took a few mouthfuls of food.

h) I felt sorry for her although the birds had escaped.

Practice

1. Add a connective and another idea to end these nursery rhyme lines. See how you can easily change story lines, for example:

> Mary had a little lamb … **until** the wolf finally gobbled it up.
> Its fleece was white as snow … **but** that was only because stayed in.
> And everywhere that Mary went … **although** not quite everywhere!
> The lamb was sure to go … **so** it became a real nuisance!

Little Miss Muffett
Sat on a tuffet,
Eating her curds and whey;
Down came a spider,
And sat down beside her,
And frightened Miss Muffet away!

Little Jack Horner,
Sat in a corner,
Eating his Christmas pie;
He put in his thumb,
And pulled out a plum,
And said, "What a good boy am I."

Barber, barber, shave a pig;
How many hairs will make a wig?
Four and twenty, that's enough:
Give the barber a pinch of snuff!

Challenger

1. Use the connectives in the box to complete the table, which shows their functions.

Location	Order	Time	Argument	Explanation
under	first	then	therefore	because

> on   next   just then   as you can see   nevertheless
> and   in other words   suddenly   after that   beside   then
> finally   or   but   until   consequently   although

Now use one word from each section in a sentence of your own.

So – what have you learned about connecting words and phrases?

Focus

Every **simple sentence** must **contain one clause**.
A simple sentence makes sense on its own.

My nose was red.

Complex sentences contain **a main clause** and **another**, **less important clause**, too.
The less important (**subordinate**) clause does not make sense by itself.

My nose was red **because I had a bad cold**.

Check it out

1. Copy these sentences and underline the verbs. Write beside each one if it is simple (S) or complex (C). Explain why. The first one has been done for you.

a) My books <u>are</u> in the desk. (S)

b) She took my books as soon as the teacher looked away.

c) Water leaks out.

d) The rain dripped slowly from the broken drainpipe.

e) Our snowman melted yesterday.

f) All the snow melted because the air temperature rose in the country.

g) I visited Paris.

h) We visited France where I saw many fascinating castles.

i) All the dogs in the kennels barked loudly.

Practice

1. Match the two sentence parts in Set A and Set B. Write the ten
complex sentences in your book.

Set A

I shall not go to Turkey
He loves rock music
It will be a disaster
His sister fainted
We called off the football match
There is a big stain on the ceiling
Mark will not give in
Stop all that noise
You will go to your room
It does not matter to me

Set B

where the water came in.
unless you tell me who broke the window.
because he plays guitar in a band.
whether or not you go to the concert.
until he finds out who stole the bike.
when she heard she had won the lottery.
although I may visit Greece.
before I get very cross.
unless I can phone him first.
so we returned the tickets.

Challenger

1. Make these simple sentences into more interesting complex ones by adding a
subordinate clause to each one. You will find examples of helpful connectives
in the 'Practice' section.

a) Sophie did not understand …

b) The rider fell off her pony …

c) It will not be possible to travel …

d) She had three stitches in her knee …

e) He visited the ancient city …

f) Margie caught measles …

g) She stood on the chair …

h) The bike will go off the road …

Now underline the subordinate clauses you have added.

**So – what have you learned about
simple and complex sentences?**

Focus

A **semi-colon** is a punctuation mark used **to separate parts of a sentence**. It is **stronger** than a **comma** but **not as strong** as a **full stop**.

Shirin loves Indian food; Marco prefers Italian food.

A **colon** is often used to introduce a list, before someone speaks, or instead of a full stop.

He was freezing cold: the temperature was below zero.

Fred said: "What are you doing here?"

The larder contained: eggs, butter, flour, fruit, and a dead mouse.

Check it out

1. Copy these sentences in your book. Replace the # with a semi-colon.

a) It was spring# the daffodils appeared almost overnight.

b) I stood quietly on the platform# soon the train would arrive.

c) Judy had not done her maths homework# she would be in trouble.

d) Sue and Maureen chatted all afternoon# they have not seen each other for years.

e) Bring me a large chocolate biscuit made from brown flour# two sticky buns, but only the round ones with cherries on the top# a large portion of steamed pudding with currants and covered in custard.

2. Copy these sentences. Replace the # with a colon.

a) You will need the following# two eggs, one kilo of flour and some milk.

b) There was only one judgement possible# death.

c) Please note the rule# no food allowed in the computer room.

d) The referee shouted# "Get off the pitch!"

Practice

1. Add semi-colons or colons to these sentences. Write out the correct versions.

a) It looked as if he had no other choice he would have to tell the truth.

b) The large wall was covered with pictures the smaller wall had nothing on it.

c) Suddenly Tricia screamed "It's a dirty great rat!" she said.

d) Elizabeth slept soundly on the bench the train passed by.

e) Take note of the school's new address 99 Arcade Street.

f) At the supermarket buy some tins of peas, but only if they are not processed some frozen chocolate cake, but look at the sell-by date and a litre of milk.

g) Please don't forget to bring these for the ski trip your passport, a woolly hat and a pair of warm gloves.

h) The woods were quiet only the birds sang in the trees.

i) I'll search the bedrooms you search the play area.

j) In the back room the cats were asleep in the kitchen the mice ate the cheese.

Challenger

1. Rewrite these advertisements from the Internet, putting in the semi-colons and colons.

Super American car for sale. This car is a fantastic bargain it is only ten years old there is not even a tiny piece of rust to be seen on it last but not least it goes like a bomb! Email Ray on raycars@raycars.co

Wanted enthusiastic music expert to work in music shop in Soho. Must have own transport. Mail address musictogo@musictogo.co

Wanted urgently someone to teach my horrible son. I want the following qualifications an ability to put up with excessive noise all day someone who can understand how the mind of an eleven-year-old works a person who can translate my son's language. Anyone desperate enough should contact helpparents@helpparents.co

Here we go all antique doll collectors Victorian, porcelain doll for sale, made in 1878. The following still original glass eyes, hair, clothes. Email Margie at margie'sdolls @margie's dolls.co

So – what have you learned about semi-colons and colons?

Unit 8 Dashes and brackets

Focus

A **dash holds words apart**. It is **stronger** than a **comma**, but not as strong as a **full stop**.

There is only one meal worth eating – spaghetti!

Brackets can be used like dashes. They can **separate off a part of a sentence** or **put in an extra example**.

He was awarded a prize in school (not before time).

Check it out

1. Copy these sentences in your book. Replace the # with a dash.

a) We have no room left in the hotel # let me repeat: no room.

b) Mark's mum # the famous actress, as I found out later # was on TV.

c) She wants to buy him a new suit # I can understand why.

d) There is only one instrument worth learning # the guitar.

e) He did not take account of the most important person # his guard.

2. Copy these sentences. Replace the # with brackets.

a) He swam across the river #as the picture showed#.

b) You must give me your homework on Wednesday. #Any homework after that will not be marked.#

c) Switch on the video recorder #see Starting Instructions on page 5#.

Practice

1. Copy the sentences below. Add dashes or brackets where they are needed.

a) He drank his tea it was already cold and moved to his desk.

b) At Cambridge University he gained a second class degree.

c) Jake got to the skateboard competition in time the competition started late.

d) The lead singer unlike the other members of the group was tidily dressed.

e) Most of the pupils lost interest the pop group had left the school.

f) The detective's disguise was not really a very effective one it was easy to see through.

g) The films all five of them lasted only a day.

h) Our Queen served caviar only the best at her banquets.

i) He bought the computer game the last in the market.

j) The chicken followed closely by all her chicks crossed the busy road.

Challenger

1. Rewrite this passage. Insert brackets and dashes where appropriate.

> More and more people young and old are taking up sailing. Look at the latest figures page 20 of the magazine which prove this.
> Good sailing and of course safe sailing is the most important thing to learn. If you are unsure of this look back at the news reports about sinking boats.
> A great deal of sport sailing, rugby, soccer is dangerous when not played well. The most important thing to learn are the rules and there are plenty in order to be safe. The law makes insurance necessary before you sail but often a fatal omission it does not cover all dangers.

So – what have you learned about dashes and brackets?

Focus

Five hundred years ago, when English began to be written down, **rules** had to be invented and '**standard English**' was said to be the '**correct**' version of **written English**. It is the kind of written English used in most books.

Non-standard English is often used in **everyday speech**. We frequently say things differently from the way in which we would write them, for example…

We have not got no money.

…is not standard English. It uses **not** and **no** together and so actually means:

We have not got any money!

Check it out

1. Choose the correct form of the verb in brackets and rewrite each sentence correctly.

a) There (was/were) two clocks on the station wall.

b) "Look. Here (are/is) the newspaper you lost yesterday," I replied.

c) My grandma (give/gave) me a new computer for Christmas.

d) All my toys (has/have) my name written on them in case they are stolen.

e) Each of the actors (was/were) given an extra clap at the end of the show.

f) Tracy (did/done) her homework before school.

g) No, Mike (aren't/isn't) allowed to go to the cinema this evening.

h) (Do/does) anybody want to go to the pantomime this year?

i) My mum (don't/doesn't) allow us to go to concerts by ourselves.

Practice

1. These sentences are written in non-standard English.
Rewrite the sentences in standard English.

a) The two boys was fighting in the street.

b) Each of the sweets in the packet were wrapped in coloured foil.

c) "I ain't done nothing," my brother shouted.

d) We done the washing up after Christmas dinner.

e) My mum said she didn't want nothing for her birthday.

f) The policewoman give me a warning when she caught me in the orchard.

g) Neither Fred nor his brother were allowed out to play.

h) I never saw nobody at the concert because the seats were at the side.

i) Louis hadn't been nowhere near the window when it smashed.

Challenger

1. Rewrite this paragraph in standard English.

"Who's got me sweets? I ain't got none left. I spent a quid on them yesterday. I bet that Ray is stuffing his face with them."

"There isn't no point in blaming me. The sweets was in my locker. Me and John was going to eat them tomorrow. I bet that bloke over there has got them."

"No. He don't know nothing. I already asked him. He give his sweets away to someone else. Those kids isn't coming today. That means we haven't got no food today."

"Wait a mo. Look in that cupboard what's to your left. I think that's the food what I bought the other day. Do anyone know if it belongs to anyone? I don't want no trouble if we eat it."

"No problem. All the adults has gone to work. Great ... this food is wicked."

So – what have you learned about standard English?

Focus

Parts of speech include the names of the word classes you have learned about so far, such as **nouns**, **verbs** and **adjectives**.

These are important because they are the words from which all sentences are made.

The **angry dog bit** the postman **viciously and** ran away.

an adjective   a noun   a verb   an adverb   a conjunction

Check it out

1. Copy these sentences. Identify the underlined parts of speech, like the first one.

a) The <u>cat</u> sat quietly on the mat. (noun)

b) We jumped over the wall and <u>fell</u> into the mud.

c) The boy loved the chocolate in the box, but he did not allow <u>her</u> any.

d) As a Christmas present, he bought me a <u>beautiful</u> gold vase.

e) Dickens wrote his novels <u>quickly</u> so they could be published in parts.

2. Add a suitable word to complete each of these sentences. Identify the part of speech you have used.

a) All the … books were piled up on the desk in front of him.

b) She … down the road feeling very happy when she received her exam results.

c) I would love a cup of … thank you very much.

d) When I bought the computer, I was told that I would need training …

e) The huge ocean liner sailed … the ocean towards the tropics.

f) … black jacket is still at the dry cleaners.

Practice

1. Copy this poem and include suitable words for each of the parts of speech.

A noun's the name of anything,
Such as ... Or ... or ... or swing.

Verbs tell us something to be done –
To ... , to ..., to ..., to run.

Conjunctions join the words together,
Such as men ... women, wind ...
weather.

Instead of nouns the pronouns
stand –
Her head, ... face, ... arm, my hand.

How things are done the adverbs tell,
Such as ..., ..., ill or well.

2. Add three more examples for each of the verses and write the words in sentences.

Challenger

1. Copy and complete the table below with suitable words.

Adjective	Noun	Verb	Adverb
blue	parrot	squawked	noisily
			enthusiastically
	elephant		
		swam	

Use the rows you have completed to make sentences. For example,

The blue parrot squawked noisily when we went past.

So – what have you learned about parts of speech in sen tences?

Focus

A **verb** is in the **active** when the subject of the verb is actually **performing the action** of the sentence. **Margaret** is the **subject** of the sentence. She is the one **performing the action**. She is mending the computer.

Margaret mended the computer.

A **verb** is **passive** when the action of the verb is being done to the subject by someone or something else in the sentence. It often uses phrases such as **was** and **were**. The **computer** is the **subject** of the sentence. The verb **to mend** applies to the computer and not to Margaret.

The computer was mended by Margaret.

Check it out

1. Copy the sentences below. Identify and underline the verbs in the active form. Circle any verbs which are in the passive form.

a) The cats killed the mice.

b) The mice were hunted by the cats.

c) I have decided upon a daring plan.

d) A plan has finally been decided upon.

e) We received your order in the post yesterday.

f) People always find mushrooms in that field.

g) Our leader was injured in a car crash.

h) We all ran over to see the accident.

Practice

1. Choose the active form of the verb in brackets to complete these sentences.

a) An old and historic parliament (was ruled by/rules) our country.

b) Members of the public over 18 (vote/were to vote) for members of Parliament.

c) The House of Lords (takes/were taken by) some votes.

d) The House of Commons (are decided by/decides) most of the laws.

e) Parliament (makes/are made by) the laws of our country.

f) The government (is ensured by/ensures) law and order in our country.

g) Parliament (invites/was invited by) the Queen to visit every year.

2. Rewrite these sentences in the passive form. For example,

Our country <u>is ruled by</u> an old and historic parliament.

Challenger

1. Rewrite this passage. Change all the active verbs to the passive form.

> Bad weather delayed our flight so we had hours to spend at the airport. We stood on the roof. Radar directed the planes in and out. Earplugs deadened the noise. We still heard some frightening noises. A girl was in trouble. Shouts directed the police to the girl. Their dog chased a man around the airport. We were worried by the delay. My sister had organised our trip for her wedding. So we sent a message to my sister. My friend found a phone. He put the money into the machine. Nothing happened and we lost the money. It was a miserable wait. Someone smashed a bottle in the distance. A lady cleaned the room.

So – what have you learned about changing active to passive?

Changing passive to active

Focus

A **verb** is **passive** when the action of the verb is being done to the subject by someone or something else in the sentence. It often uses phrases such as **was** and **were**. The **shovel** is the **subject** of the sentence. The verb **to oil** applies to the shovel and not to Lisa.

The shovel **was oiled** by Lisa.

A **verb** is in the **active** when the subject of the verb is actually performing the action of the sentence. **Lisa** is the **subject** of the sentence. She is the one performing the action. She is oiling the shovel.

Lisa **oiled** the shovel.

Check it out

1. Copy and complete the table. Write the active and the passive verbs from the sentences into the correct columns.

Active verbs	Passive verbs

a) That knife has wounded me.

b) We sat on the bench by the river.

c) They were amazed by the size of the crowd.

d) All the books were taken out of the library.

e) Mike took the bike back to the shop.

f) The flat looked good until they moved in.

g) Trevor kept his promise and gave her the money.

Practice

1. Copy and complete the sentences by matching the passive sentence to its active one.

Trout are found in this stream.	Aunt Sophie looks after my sister.
The new submarine was launched by the Queen last week.	Microwaves power the new printer.
My sister is looked after by Aunt Sophie.	People find trout in this stream.
Our car was parked by students.	The Queen launched the new submarine last week.
The new printer is powered by microwaves.	The police examined my bag.
My bag was examined by the police.	Students parked our car.

Now add two more examples to the table. Underline the subject of the sentence in each example and circle each verb.

2. Explain the differences between a sentence in the passive and the active form.

Challenger

1. Rewrite this passage. Change all the passive verbs to the active form.

A scream was made by Sarah. Immediately, four guards were seized by the villains and dragged to the Master's feet. Then John was tied up. But the guards' attack was seen by Superman. His foot was stuck out and one villain was caught in mid air. He was then pinned to the wall. Mercy was begged for by the creature. Sarah was looked at by Superman. Should the villain be released or sent to prison?

So – what have you learned about changing passive to active?

Focus

Formal styles of writing are used for 'formal' situations. The language used is very **different from spoken** language.

- You find formal styles on **official** forms. For example, you might see 'forename' rather than 'first name'.

- You could find it in **official buildings** on signs. For example, you might see 'Personnel are requested to walk independently' rather than an order such as, 'Walk in single file'.

- It is often found in important rules and regulations. For example you might see 'Smoking is prohibited' rather than 'Smoking is not allowed'.

Check it out

1. Match the formal, official word in Set A with its meaning in Set B. Write them out in your book. Use a dictionary to help.

Set A	Set B
Forename	A copy of something.
Marital status	A woman's name before marriage.
Duplicate	Capital letters.
Maiden name	The country you come from.
Block letters	Your first name.
On the reverse	The work that you do.
Nationality	On the back of something.
Occupation	If you are married or single.

Practice

1. Copy and complete the table below. Use the words in the box.
   Use a dictionary to find out what the words mean.

Formal words	Informal words
beverages	drinks

> eat   distinguishing marks   dwelling   pay   endorse
> consume   superior   reside   drinks   citizenship   scars
> hide   beverages   reverse   house   request   ask   sign
> the back   remuneration   boss   conceal   live

Challenger

1. Read the examples of formal, official language below. Say where you think
   the expressions might be used.

a) Personnel are requested to enter independently.

b) Attention: maintain due vigilance during experimental activities.

c) Vehicular travel is prohibited.

d) These areas are primarily intended for pedestrian use.

e) We are in receipt of your communication of last week.

f) The management cannot accept liability for loss or theft.

g) We have pleasure in forwarding the goods ordered.

h) We apologise for any inconvenience incurred.

i) I have insufficient resources for the purchase of refreshments.

Now write what you think the expressions mean in clearer, simpler English.

So – what have you learned about formal official language?

Focus

A **clause** is a **group of words**. It can be used as a **whole sentence** or a **part** of a sentence.

It must contain a **verb** and a **subject**.

Tracey walked home.

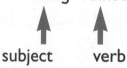

subject   verb

Check it out

1. Copy these clauses. Circle the verb in each example and underline each subject. The first one has been done for you.

a) Because <u>I</u> (loved) it.

b) If you press that button.

c) She stayed in the garden.

d) He could reach the books.

e) When it stops raining.

f) Her coat was torn.

g) Although it is green.

h) So he will win.

Practice

1. Match the single clause sentences below. Add a connective from the box to
make each pair into one sentence. Do it like this:

The car broke down in the rain <u>but</u> it started again when it dried out.

a) The car broke down in the rain.   It was freezing cold outside.

b) The crow flew away.   He gives evidence in court.

c) My dad drove all night.   The security was important.

d) My nose was bright red.   It started again when it dried out.

e) We drank warm cocoa.   We finished building the bonfire.

f) I was allowed to open my presents.   I can get it published.

g) A policeman must wear a uniform.   The hunter with a gun arrived.

h) I am writing my story.   My father arrived at the party.

i) The Queen was arriving.   He was too tired to drive.

> when   because   but   after   so   when   before   although

Challenger

1. Complete these sentences by adding new clauses of your own.

a) I will not go to the concert because …

b) She left the classroom party before …

c) The roof will not be mended unless …

d) You will not find the map until …

e) It was a sunny day so …

f) Sheila could not make out whether …

g) The wicked stepmother disappeared when …

h) The police inspector could not think how …

So – what have you learned about clauses?

Focus

A **simple sentence** must contain **one clause**.
A simple sentence makes sense on its own.

Pinocchio's nose grew bigger.

Complex sentences contain a **main clause** and another,
less important clause, too. The less important
(subordinate) clause does not make sense by itself.

Pinocchio's nose grew bigger **as he told more lies**.

Check it out

1. Copy the sentences below. Circle the main clause in each sentence and
underline the subordinate clause. Do it like this:

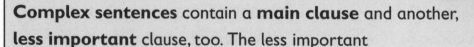

(The fisherman caught a pike) <u>after he waited for an hour</u>.

a) He scored the goal when the keeper was injured on the ground.

b) The red car shot around the corner and crashed into the tree.

c) John's jacket was cheap but looked expensive.

d) I will not go out tonight because I have a headache.

e) Because I do not like her, I will not share my lunch.

f) If I go to the film, I will sit by myself.

Practice

1. Join each pair of sentences below. Use the pronoun **who**, for example,

Dickens wrote Oliver Twist. He was a famous novelist.

Dickens, <u>who</u> wrote Oliver Twist, was a famous novelist.

a) Charlie Chaplin was a famous comedian. He died a while ago.

b) The Italian used to play for an English team. He now manages a French team.

c) Robin Hood lived in Nottingham. He robbed the rich to give to the poor.

d) My mum is a great mechanic. She owns the garage around the corner.

e) John Lennon was a member of the Beatles. He died in New York.

2. Join each pair of sentences below using the pronoun **which**.

You will need to rearange the words.

a) The table is an antique. It is two hundred years old.

b) The football match was between two London teams. It ended after the first goal.

c) Fresh strawberries are good for the skin. They not always available.

d) The Rocky mountains are parallel to the coast. They get most of the rain.

e) The Police force was founded by Robert Peel. It celebrated its anniversary recently.

Challenger

1. Join these pairs of sentences using suitable connectives.

Write each example out as one sentence.

a) No one will leave the class. The Headteacher has made her choice.

b) You need to learn to swim. You can perform lifesaving.

c) His father bought him a new computer. He should have waited for the sales.

d) My cousin was very confident. He did not pass the exam.

e) Drive for an hour. You pass an old church with a steeple.

So – what have you learned about complex sentences?

Focus

A **simple sentence** must contain **one clause**.
A simple sentence makes sense on its own.

The pears tasted sweet.

Complex sentences contain a **main clause** and another, **less important clause**, too. The less important (subordinate) clause does not make sense by itself.

The pears tasted sweet **when they ripened**.

Check it out

1. Copy the sentences below. Circle the main clause in each sentence and underline the subordinate clause. The first one has been done for you.

a) (The video was so dull) that I fell asleep.

b) The market stall was not making them enough money so they sold it.

c) When I am seventeen, I am allowed to get a driving licence.

d) Until I check with my mum, I can't tell you if I can go out tomorrow.

e) Get that mess cleaned up in the kitchen before I tell your mother!

f) You will never find the secret plans unless you look in the right place.

g) While the police looked through the house, I searched the bin.

Practice

1. Change these two-clause sentences into one single-clause sentence.
Use commas to join the groups of sentences, for example,

Venice is a city in Italy. It has many canals.
Venice, a city in Italy, has many canals.

a) Athens is the capital of Greece. It is famous for the Parthenon.

b) Manchester is a city in the north. It has excellent road communications.

c) Roald Dahl is the author of many children's books. He died a few years ago.

d) Tennis is a popular summer sport. It is played outside from May to September.

e) Silk is made from the pupa of silkworms. It makes fine material.

f) Albert Einstein was a famous mathematician. He discovered many things.

g) French is taught to many children in schools. It is a useful European language.

h) Diwali is the festival of lights. It is an important Hindu celebration.

Challenger

1. Join these three sentences using suitable connectives and commas.
Write each example out as one sentence.

a) The cat walked out of the tall grass. She crawled slowly along. She finally jumped on the poor mouse.

b) I climbed on the coach. I paid my fare. I travelled to London.

c) You go swimming in the pool. You need to be sure it is safe. You will take a risk.

d) I cannot carry that bag. It hurts me. I broke my arm last week.

e) The marathon runner stopped to breathe. He stopped by the finishing post.

f) The driver stopped at the lights. He shouted at the girl pedestrian. She had nearly run in front of the car.

So – what have you learned about complex sentences?

Focus

A **conditional verb** tells you that the action **might** happen, because it **depends on something** or **somebody** else. **Should**, **would** and **could** are the three words which tell you if a verb is conditional.

We **would** go to the cinema if …

I **should** be grateful if you could …

He **could** do his homework although …

Check it out

1. Copy the sentences. Underline the conditional verbs, like the first one.

a) I <u>should be</u> grateful if you would send me some information.

b) I could not eat the chocolate as it was bitter.

c) I told you that you would be sorry.

d) If I could do tapestry like that, I would be proud.

e) If you are tired, you should go to bed.

f) We would not let him out until he gave us back the bag.

g) Could I borrow that video if I promise to return it tomorrow?

h) She would have passed her exams if she had done more work.

i) If the weather is fine, we should be able to go on a picnic.

Practice

1. Match together the halves of these sentences. Write them out correctly. Underline the words which tell you which sentences are conditional.

If I water the garden	I will be rich.
If I had watered the garden	I will scream and shout.
If I had taken the money	the grass will grow.
If I take the money	I would have screamed and shouted.
If she pulls my hair again	the grass would have grown.
If she had pulled my hair again	I would have been rich.

2. Explain the difference between each pair of sentences.

Challenger

1. Complete the conditional sentences with suitable endings.

a) I should …

b) If I had …

c) Could I …

d) Would you …

e) The cat could …

f) When she had …

2. a) Write five conditional sentences of your own. Use some of the sentence constructions you have read in the other Units.

b) Explain what makes conditional sentences different from other verb tenses.

So – what have you learned about conditionals?

Focus

A **conditional verb** tells you that the action might happen, because it depends on something or somebody else. **Should**, **would** and **could** are the three words which usually tell you if a verb is conditional. Conditionals can be in the **past** and the **future** tense:

We **would** have gone to the shops if …

I **will** be grateful if you could …

She **will have to** do her sums although …

Check it out

1. Copy the sentences below. Underline the conditional verbs and say if they are in the past (P) or in the future (F) tense. The first one has been done for you.

a) She <u>will be going</u> to the ball if the Fairy Godmother arrives. (F)

b) If I don't work harder, I will have to leave school.

c) If I had passed my driving test the first time, I would not be so desperate.

d) Whether she found it or not, she would have to tell her father.

e) You will not find a better holiday in the world than here.

f) If you had got up earlier you would have seen the sunset.

g) We will have to tell him tonight before the post arrives tomorrow.

h) No one would notice if you left the party early.

Practice

1. Copy and complete the tables below. Write four other conditional sentences of your own in each box. Follow the rules.

If ... (present tense)	I will ...
If I pass the exam	I will go to university.

If ... (past tense)	I would ...
If I passed the exam	I would go to university.

If ... had ... (past tense)	I would have ...
If I had passed the exam	I would have gone to university.

Challenger

1. Copy these pairs of sentences. Underline the conditional verbs.

a) My mum could be given help in the house.
   My mum should be given help in the house.

b) Trevor should pass his driving test in my car.
   Trevor passed his driving test in my car.

c) I would give them all my money for charity.
   I should give them all my money for charity.

2. Explain how the meanings of these groups of sentences are different because of the different tenses of the verbs used.

So – what have you learned about conditionals?

Focus

We often shorten sentences to make notes. Sometimes, we can use **abbreviations**: USA for United States of America.

Sometimes, we can use **fewer words**: A place where fish are kept in a house – an aquarium.

Sometimes, we can **combine sentences** into shorter ones:
The car stopped working. It stopped because it ran out of petrol.
The car stopped working because it ran out of petrol.

Services

Check it out

1. Match the abbreviations below to their meanings. Write them in your book.

Abbreviation	Meaning
pto	anonymous
kph	Road
Rd	Avenue
anon	please turn over
Ave	kilometres per hour

2. Write out the abbreviations for these. Use a dictionary to help.

United States of America   Before Christ   Square
Royal Society for the Prevention of Cruelty to Animals   Post Office

Practice

1. Give one word for each of the following places. Use a dictionary to help.

a) Where fish are kept in the house.   c) Where race horses are kept.

b) Where ships are unloaded.   d) Where plays are performed.

2. Write one word for each of the following. Use a dictionary to help.

a) A device for putting out a fire.   c) To leave a country to live in another.

b) To rub out.   d) A building for the treatment of sick people.

3. Write one or two words which summarise the following. Use a dictionary.

a) pigs, cows, goats, horses, sheep, chickens **– animals**

b) radio, magazines, TV, film, newspapers

c) curtains, blinds, armchairs, dining table, cushions

d) teachers, accountants, lawyers, vicars

Challenger

1. Combine each of these pairs of sentences into one shorter sentence.
   The first example shows you what to miss out (in brackets).

a) The car stopped working(. It stopped) because it ran out of petrol.

b) We shall visit the zoo. We shall visit it as soon as possible.

c) The workers squeezed the grapes. They squeeze them to get the wine.

d) The water drains away. It drains through the hole in the bucket.

e) The fisherman lifted the fish. It was lifted clear out of the water.

f) The remark was typical. It was typical of my sister.

g) My mother is in hospital. She is there to have an operation.

h) Our house is made of wood. It is built like this because it is cheap.

**So – what have you learned about
different ways of shortening sentences?**

Focus

When you **edit your work**, you make sure you have written what you really mean to say. It is your chance to **change** things before a final copy is made. Sometimes you have to **contract** (make shorter) your sentences, sometimes you have to **combine** sentences in better ways.

He was reversing backwards out of the garage.

Reversing and **backwards** mean the same thing. So why say the same thing twice?

He was reversing out of the garage.

Check it out

1. Make these sentences shorter. Take out all the **adjectives** and **adverbs** (describing words).

a) Our **small**, **black** cat **quietly** chased the **grey** mouse into its **dark** hole.

b) My long-lost uncle from Italy sat down quietly and ordered a very expensive alcoholic drink.

c) The small, fair-haired girl from next door loved, above anything else, diving dramatically into the blue waters of the pool.

d) The brightly-painted clown, dressed in the wildest colours imaginable, fell comically from the white horse into the sand of the arena.

e) My favourite cousin, Sarah, read her new storybook enthusiastically.

f) Our new guest at the hotel, the famous film star, quickly phoned the local police.

g) Jim, my very favourite singer from my very favourite band, kindly signed my leather-covered, battered autograph book.

Practice

1. Decide on the most important facts in these sentences and write them out as briefly as possible. For example, **The group of students attempted to climb the mountain but they did not reach the summit of the mountain.** <u>**Climbing students failed to reach top of mountain.**</u>

a) Two men were killed yesterday when their car hit a petrol lorry.

b) The staff meeting at the school started at three o'clock in the afternoon.

c) The ancient Egyptians covered their dead bodies with exotic preserving oils and then wrapped them up carefully in bandages.

d) The Oscar for the best actress in a supporting role in a film this year has been awarded to Sarah Biggs – a previously unknown girl.

e) Our new car was of a very large size and was red in colour.

f) They were outnumbered by the pirates, but yet, however, they would not give up.

g) They rescued all of the important things from the flood waters, such as, for example, their blankets, the food, some fresh water.

Challenger

1. Edit this passage. Write the four things that Pat had to do in the fewest words possible.

> Pat was really busy. She had to do several things on her way home from school. First she had to collect her baby sister from nursery and then she had to call into the supermarket to buy a bottle of milk for their breakfast. Hopefully they would have some more left. In her pocket was the electricity bill she needed to pay as well and ... oh, there was the car to clean before she was allowed to have her tea.

So – what have you learned about shortening sentences?

Focus

The **purpose** of **reports** is to **describe the way things are**. They try to make the information as clear as possible to the reader.

A report:

- could be a guide book
- could be a report on your project on dinosaurs
- could be a description of a scene.

Check it out

1. Read this passage and answer the questions.

a) Copy the report. Underline the verbs. Which tense are they in?

b) Write facts about bats that you could check in another reference book.

c) Does the writer talk about one particular bat or about bats in general?

d) Underline the pronouns.

e) Do you have to put your facts in a certain order when you are writing a report? Explain your answer.

f) Would a diagram or picture would help you understand the information better? Why?

In Britain there are fourteen species of bat. These bats live in the south and west of England. There are very few bats in Scotland. All the bats are small. On average they weigh 4 g and have a wing span of 20 cm. There are a few myths about bats. 'As blind as a bat' is completely wrong. Bats can see, but not in colour. Bats are under threat now more than most other wildlife.

Practice

1. This report sounds strange because the verbs are in the wrong tense. Rewrite it. Put the verbs into the present tense.

> Metals were an essential part of our lives. Most of the metals we used began their lives in the earth. An ore was a mixture of metal and other rock. When we made alloys we made it like toffee. We placed all the ingredients in a pan and heated it. The ore turned to liquid and was poured off. The process of extracting the metal from ore was called smelting.

2. Copy these sentences from a report. Add suitable clauses to complete them.

a) The match will not light again because …

b) Gas will cause an explosion if …

c) Water expands when freezing so …

d) It is best to plant seeds when …

e) Heavy objects will sink in water although …

Challenger

1. Write your own report using one of the subjects below.

a) A report about your school.

b) A report on your latest project.

c) A description of the scene outside the classroom window.

Try to follow this plan:

● write a general opening about your subject

● include some more detail

● describe some things in real detail: functions, qualities, habits

● include a comparison with something else

● write a conclusion.

So – what have you learned about the features of reports?

Focus

The purpose of a **recount** is to **retell information** or to **give someone an account of events**.

A recount:

- could be a description of a scene
- could be a recount of a visit to a farm
- could be a newspaper account
- could be a biography.

Check it out

1. One feature of a recount is the use of the **past tense**. Rewrite these sentences. Change the verbs into the past tense.

a) Tracy goes to nursery every day. She learns how to write.

b) I begin school in the autumn and leave the following term.

c) Mike swims the river every year and climbs exhausted on the bank.

d) My mum forgets the sweets and gives me an apple.

e) Jim writes the cheque and gives it to him.

f) I forget my lunch so I eat a chocolate bar.

2. Another feature of a recount is writing events in **chronological order** (in the correct time sequence). Rewrite these instructions on how to make toast. Put the events into the correct order.

- Finally, eat it!
- First, cut some bread.
- Then select the cooking time on the dial of the toaster.
- You need an electric toaster.
- When the toast pops up, remove it and butter it.
- Insert the bread.

Practice

1. Copy this passage.

> The bank in the High Street was full of bored people. Robert and I stood in a queue and watched impatiently when, suddenly, we saw the man in black suddenly barge through the doors.
>
> "What shall we do?" I whispered.
>
> Before Robert could reply, the alarm rang. Next, the thief looked around him, threw down the bag and ran.
>
> This was a frightening experience and I would not like to live through it again.

a) Circle the pronouns. What do you notice?

b) Underline the verbs. Which tense is used?

c) What information does the writer give you? In what order is it given to you?

d) How does the writer set the scene in the bank?

e) Which people are involved? Are they named or left anonymous?

f) Underline connectives and words which start the sentences. How do they help to move the recount forward?

Challenger

1. Choose one of the examples below.

a) A visit to …

b) A famous person we have studied in history is …

Write your own recount text using these features:

- set the scene
- use **I** or **we** pronouns
- use connectives such as **next** … **then** … **after that** … **finally** …
- finish with a sentence which sums up the events.
- describe events in order
- be accurate in your description of people

So – what have you learned about the features of recounts?

Focus

> When you give someone **instructions**, you describe how
> something is made or done in a **clear** and **ordered way**.

You:

● could instruct someone how to get from
your house to school

● could write a recipe

● could tell someone how to programme
your video machine to record.

Check it out

1. Copy these sentences. Change the verbs to use the imperative (command)
form that is used in instructions. For example, **May I take a sweet?** becomes
Take a sweet.

a) It is possible to switch off the computer.

b) Fred can pull the joystick of his computer game.

c) Would you care to eat another biscuit?

d) My teacher asked me to write out the spellings.

e) The bus conductor asked me to sit down and be quiet.

2. Rewrite these instructions. Use some of the connectives in the box to make
them sound better.

> Leave the house. Turn right. Walk for ten minutes. Turn left. Stop at the
> bus stop. Cross the road. Walk up the side street. Enter the market.

> first   then   next   therefore   before
> insert   after that   soon   and

Practice

1. Read the instructions to paint a wall.

a) Copy the instructions. Underline the verbs. Do instructions use a special form of the verb?

b) How is this kind of writing set out differently from many other kinds of writing?

c) Why is a list of equipment so important with instructions? Where should it be written in the instructions?

d) Why is writing an event in the correct order so important in a set of instructions?

e) Would a diagram make the instructions clearer? Why?

Painting a wall

You need: a large paint brush, emulsion paint, protective clothing, coverings to protect furnishings.

Procedure: Paint large areas a little at a time. Paint vertical stripes first, then make cross-strokes to join them. Do not put any more paint on your brush. Continue to smooth gently – back into the painted area. Limit yourself to a small area so the paint does not dry too quickly.

Challenger

1. Write your own set of instructions. Choose a subject from the ones below.

a) Instruct someone how to get from your house to school.

b) Write instructions how to make a paper aeroplane.

c) Tell someone how to programme your video machine to record.

Follow these four steps:

- write down what you are trying to do and give your writing a title
- write a list of the materials or equipment you need
- write down the steps you need to take in the correct order.

Decide if a diagram would be helpful.

So – what have you learned about features of instructions?

Focus

Advertising is the best example of promotional language.
Language is used to **persuade** and **influence** people.

Check it out

1. Sometimes advertising may twist language in a clever way
to attract your attention.
Explain which sort of products you think these signs are
advertising. Give your reasons.

a) SPRAYTION

b) *EZEECLENE*

c) CHOC U LIKE

d) **The plaice for chips**

e) **TCUP**

f) **CUTZ 4 U**

g) ***DRIVEFAST***

Practice

1. Write down the comparative and superlative forms of the adjectives in the box.

> strong   lucky   thin   good   beautiful   lovely   handsome

strong	stronger	strongest

2. Use a thesaurus to find as many synonyms as possible that an advertiser might want to use for **good** and **big** to describe certain products.

3. Rewrite this dull advert. Make it sound more interesting to your reader. Put in more detail and try to persuade the reader that it is a good item to buy.

> FOR SALE. Dishwasher, one year old. Good working order. As seen on TV. £100

Challenger

1. Write your own advertisement for TV, cinema or radio. Decide on a product you would like to sell, (perhaps a new brand of training shoes or a new kind of mountain bike). Here are some possible approaches to your advertisement:

- this product will make you and your family happy
- good-looking people use the product
- only a select few have the product
- it is luxurious and expensive
- you will be popular if you have the product.

Use words to do with science, technical words, words like **NEW**, jokes, pictures of animals and babies, free offers to attract your customers …

> So – what have you learned about the language of promotion?

Focus

You write **explanations** to **answer questions**.

What is the water cycle?

How do you copy work from the computer onto a disk?

Why did the dinosaurs die out?

Check it out

1. Read the explanation below and answer the questions.

> Locks are built to control the flow of rivers. They let boats move up- or down-stream, but prevent water from being wasted. Locks are small and are usually made of two gates which are closed to let water escape or to pump it in. This is how boats can travel upstream. A series of locks is like a flight of stairs.

a) Copy the passage and underline the verbs. What tense are they written in?

b) Explanations start with an introduction or introductory statement. What is the introductory statement in this passage?

c) Is there any order in the way the information is written down?

d) What kinds of diagrams would help the explanation more?

e) Make up your own questions about the passage using **what, how, why,** for example, "Why are the locks made of two gates?"

f) Most explanations are written in an impersonal style. Is there anything personal in this explanation? Would personal writing be an appropriate style for this kind of writing?

Practice

1. Often, explanations use the passive voice. Copy this passage and change the verbs into the passive form.

> The dog pulled his master up the road. His uncle met him and joked with him. When he arrived at school his teacher told him off for being late.

2. Copy these sentences. Add an appropriate beginning or end to each sentence. Join it to the rest of the sentence by using connectives to do with time, for example, **then**, **next**, **after**.

a) Some people believe a meteor crashed to the earth …

b) … the Ice Age arrived to kill the dinosaurs.

c) … new animals evolved from the dinosaurs who had survived.

3. Copy these sentences. Add an appropriate beginning or end to each sentence. Join it to the rest of the sentence by using connectives to do with cause and effect, for example, **because**, **so**, **this results in**, **therefore**.

a) Plants grow upwards …

b) … this is important to growth.

c) If you do not give a plant enough sunlight …

d) … we can prove the need for light.

Challenger

1. Write an explanation of your own, such as 'How to get your class computer to print out your work'. Use the following steps:

● write an introduction to the topic

● explain each step, one by one, in the process

● finish the process.

So – what have you learned about the features of explanations?

Focus

Often, in written **discussions** or **arguments**, you need to **persuade** your reader or put forward your **point of view**.

You could write a letter to a newspaper disagreeing with foxhunting.

You could write a brochure trying to get someone to give you money for sick animals.

You could write an advertisement for a new pair of training shoes.

Check it out

1. Read the letter about foxhunting and answer the questions.

> Foxhunting is cruel and I believe it should be banned. Every thinking person in this country knows they are hunted just for fun. To prove this, I talked to a shepherd last week who saw one defencelessly killed. Did you know the fox was really helping the country and is not a nuisance at all? In fact, it helps to keep down harmful pests.

a) Copy the passage and underline the opening statement.

b) Is this a personal or an impersonal statement? Which words tell you?

c) How many different arguments does the writer use?

d) Underline the verbs. What tense has been used?

e) List some of the connective words and phrases the writer has used for the argument, for example, **To prove this ...**

Practice

1. a) Copy the passage. Change the verbs in this argument to the simple present tense so it sounds better, for example, **Cats <u>are</u> a nuisance.**

> Cats were a nuisance. They have continually dug up my flowerbeds and scratched my lawn. They needed to be kept in by their owners. If I saw another one in my garden I chased it away.

b) Add four more sentences to the argument. Keep to the simple present tense.

2. Arguments (persuasive writing) often use logical connectives such as **therefore, this shows, however, because** to prove their points.
Write some sentences of your own to support one of these points of view:
School uniform should/should not be worn.
Use some of the connectives in your argument.

Challenger

1. Try to persuade someone that **Smoking is bad for your health**.
Follow this plan:

- Write an opening statement explaining your point of view.
- Make a point, giving some detail and a reason.
- Make another point, giving some detail and a reason.
- Make another point, giving some detail and a reason.
- Use connectives such as: **Indeed** … **However** …

  For example … **To conclude** …
- Come back to your main argument. Summarise your reasons.
- Show how you have proved your point by writing **Therefore** …

So – what have you learned about the language of persuasion?

Focus

A **discussion** should present **all** sides of an argument to your reader, **not** just what you think. You should give arguments and information from various points of view.

> I believe that school holidays are too long. However, I can understand that many people think children and teachers need a rest from each other.

Discussions often use **reported speech**.

Check it out

1. Read this passage from a discussion.

> In Britain, road accidents to do with drink-driving are the commonest cause of death in young people. I believe that people who drink and drive are not only being stupid with their own lives but are also selfish because they endanger the lives of others. People can be crippled for life through no fault of their own.

a) Copy the passage and underline the verbs. Which tense are they in?

b) Underline the first sentence. How does it introduce the discussion?

c) Write out one argument from the passage and the evidence that is given to prove it.

2. Copy and complete these three sentences with a suitable ending. Note how the underlined connectives can make your argument stronger.

a) Young drivers cause most accidents, <u>because</u> …

b) They often drive faster, <u>therefore</u> …

c) Many people think they should not drive alone, <u>however</u> …

Practice

1. Write these speeches as reported speech.
Do it like this: **Miss Jones: I do not want to inhale other people's smoke. It is unhealthy** becomes **Miss Jones said that she did not want to inhale other people's smoke. It was not healthy.**

a) Doctor Smith: A person who smokes every day will endanger their health.

b) Jim: I don't like being in a room full of smokers. My clothes start to smell.

c) Nita: There is nothing wrong with smoking. I should be free to do what I like.

d) My teacher: If I catch any of you smoking I will be very disappointed.

2. Change this direct speech to reported speech. Do it like this:
"Why do you want to smoke?" the teacher asked.
The teacher asked why he wanted to smoke.

a) "It doesn't make you look any more important," my mum said.

b) "All Ranjit wants is to look cool," said Reena.

c) "I smoke all the time with my friends," boasted Jimmy.

d) 'I think that you are wasting your time and money," replied Chris.

Challenger

Write your own discussion of this topic: **The arguments for and against children being given homework.** Use the following plan to help:

1. Explain the topic for discussion.

2. Give one argument and some evidence.

3. Give an opposing argument and some evidence.

4. Repeat points 2 and 3 with another argument

5. say what you believe and write your conclusion.

So – what have you learned about discursive language?

Focus

Formal styles of writing are used for **formal situations**.

- You find formal styles on **official forms** you need to complete.

- You could find it in **official buildings** on signs.

- It is often found in **important rules** and **regulations**.

Some people say that using such language makes understanding easier.

Some people say it is old-fashioned and makes understanding much more difficult.

Check it out

1. Copy and complete the table below. Use the sentences from the box and write them in the correct column.

Formal style of letter	Informal style of letter

> Dear Sir or Madam   Yours faithfully   Dear Mum   Cheers Jim
> I hope this finds you in the best of health   How are you?   Best wishes
> Yours sincerely   I refer to your letter of last month   love and kisses

2. Which type of letter is written in a more friendly way? Why do you think this is?

Practice

1. Copy these sentences from the emergency procedure leaflet on an aeroplane.

a) For your safety you must comply with all the signs.

b) Emergency exit: cabin door operation.

c) Seats 6A and 6B are designated as emergency seats only.

d) If you meet these criteria, please identify the exit nearest to you.

e) Review the information on the back of this card.

f) Keep your belt fastened unless crew assistance is required.

g) Infant flotation devices are available.

h) Identify yourself to a crewmember to be re-seated.

i) To sit in the exit seat you must be independent of responsibilities for another person.

Underline the words which are examples of formal writing.

2. Rewrite the examples. Use simpler, less formal words.

3. Which do you think are the best instructions to have on a plane? Why?

Challenger

1. Rewrite this application form in less formal language. Complete the form as if you were an adult.

Applicant's surname ....
Full Christian names ....
Maiden name ....
Marital status ....
Name of spouse ....
Distinguishing marks ....
Country of residence ....
Nationality ....
Previous occupation and employer
....
Dependants ....
Contact number ....
Signature ....
The countersignatory should also endorse the reverse side of one photograph.

You may redeem the voucher according to the instructions on the reverse.

Return this at your earliest convenience.

So – what have you learned about formal styles of writing?

Focus

Slang	Groups of people who speak the same language, often invent words to make their language special and private, such as **I'm wearing my whistle and flute** (suit).
Accent	People speak the same language but it sounds different because of the way they say it, so **Toity poiple boids** could be someone from New York saying **Thirty purple birds**.
Dialect	People may speak the same language but they have completely different words for things and ways of saying them, so a Jamaican writer might say, **Him head eena de air** for **He kept his head in the air**.

Check it out

1. Read these examples of Cockney rhyming slang.

   Match each slang phrase to its meaning.

   Slang phrase

   Whistle and flute
   Apples and pears
   Trouble and strife
   Barnet fair
   Plates of meat
   Loaf of bread
   North and south
   Bees and honey

   Rhyme

   The wife
   Feet
   My head
   Your mouth
   A suit
   Hair
   Money
   The stairs

Practice

1. Copy and complete the table below. What words do we use for these American words and phrases? Use a dictionary for help.

American word or expression	What we would use	American word or expression	What we would use
Clothes pins	Clothes pegs	Chips	
An elevator		An apartment	
Vest		Checkers	
Sidewalk		Subway	
Ice-box		Trunk	

2. Add four more examples to the table and test them on a friend.

Challenger

1. Afferbeck Lauder in his book *Let's Talk Strine* wrote down how he thought Australians talked. Read these examples to yourself and write out what you think the writer wanted you to understand, like **scettin lairder = it's getting louder!** Try it and you can talk in an Australian accent without even trying!

a) It gives me grape leisure …

b) Thenk smite.

   Dimension.

c) I got asplit nair dyke.

d) Fitwer smeeide go.

e) I gunga din, the door slokt.

2. Watch some Australian TV programmes and make a list of words that Australians use and we do not, for example, **ute** is used for a small truck or van. Make a class collection.

So – what have you learned about in your language investigation?

Focus

This Unit looks at the **history** of the English language. Because the United Kingdom has been invaded so many times over the centuries, **new languages** have been **introduced**. This makes our language very rich and interesting.

- The Romans left us Latin words such as **century** and **audio**.
- The French left us with new word endings such as **garage**, **ballet** and **café**.
- The Vikings left us with short, hard-sounding words such as **skirt** and **knife**.
- The Greeks left us with new science words such as **microscope** and **biology**.

Check it out

You could be surprised how easy it is to read words written hundreds of years ago – language has not changed that much.

Latin or Greek	Meaning	Two examples of words
nova (Latin)	new	novel novelty
photo (Greek)	light	
bi (Latin)		bicycle
-ology (Greek)	a study of	
centum (Latin)		century
bio (Greek)	life	
micro (Greek)		microscope
audio (Latin)		audible

Practice

1. Copy and complete the table below to show the influence of Latin and Greek words in English. Use a dictionary to help you

2. Read and copy this passage written in 1490 by William Caxton.

> And the good wyfe answerde that she coude speke no frenshe. And the marchaunt was angry for he also coude speke no frenshe, but wold have hadde egges and she understode hym not. And thenne at laste a nother sayd that he wolde have eyren*. Then the good wyf sayd that she understod hym wel.

* a regional word for eggs.

a) Underline the words which you cannot understand.

b) Where could you look to find out about them?

Challenger

1. Copy the passage from Shakespeare's play *Macbeth* written four hundred years ago.

1st witch:	Round about the cauldron go
	In the poisoned entrails throw.
	Toad that under cold stone
	Days and nights hath thirty-one
	Swelter'd venom sleeping got,
	Boil thou first i' th' charmed pot.
All:	Double, double, toil and trouble,
	Fire burn, and cauldron bubble.

a) Say how you know this passage is from a play.

b) Why do you think Shakespeare chose to rhyme this speech?

c) Underline any words you do not understand.

d) See if you can find the words in a modern dictionary.

e) What makes this more difficult to understand: the words used or the way the sentences are written?

f) What are the witches doing?

g) Write a modern version.

So – has language changed that much over hundreds of years?

Range of Books Available

Year 3 Sentence	Year 4 Sentence	Year 5 Sentence	Year 6 Sentence
Year 3 Word	Year 4 Word	Year 5 Word	Year 6 Word

Literacy Differentiation Sentence Level Year 6

First published 1999
Reprinted 1999, 2000

Letts Educational,
9–15 Aldine Street, London W12 8AW
Tel: 020 8740 2270 Fax: 020 8740 2280

Text © Louis Fidge and Ray Barker

Illustrations © Phil Burrows, Richard Duszsczak, Simon Girling & Associates (Liz Sawyer), John Plumb, Sylvie Poggio Artists Agency (Simon Jacobs) and Ken Vail Graphic Design (Liz Bryan)

Designed by Ken Vail Graphic Design, Cambridge

British Library Cataloguing-in-Publication Data
A CIP record for this book is available from the British Library

ISBN: 1 84085 238 0

Printed in the UK by Ashford Colour Press

Letts Educational Ltd, a division of Granada Learning Ltd. Part of the Granada Media Group.